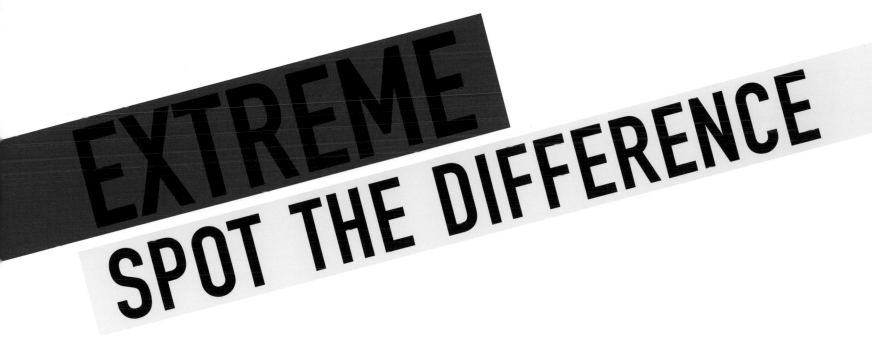

Published in 2014 by
Carlton Books Ltd
20 Mortimer Street
London W1T 3JW

ISBN 978-1-78097-493-4

10 9 8 7 6 5 4 3 2

Printed and bound in China

The publishers would like to thank the following sources for their kind permission to reproduce
the pictures in this book.

Getty Images: /Peter Adams/Photolibrary: 36-37, 78-79; /David Cannon: 60-61; /G. Fiume/
Maryland Terrapins: 48-49; /Paul Gilham: 32-33; /Philipp Klinger: 44-45; /Bernhard Lang/Stone:
40-41; /Jean-Pierre Lescourret/Lonely Planet Images: 34-35; /Rachel Lewis/Lonely Planet
Images: 68-69; /Douglas Mason: 28-29; /Martin Poole/The Image Bank: 52-53; /Christophe
Simon/AFP: 18-19; /Dave Stamboulis/Age Fotostock: 70-71; /Benoit Stichelbaut/Hemis.fr: 80-83;
/Oliver Strewe/Lonely Planet Images: 38-39; /Harald Sund/Brand X Pictures: 20-21; /Konrad
Wothe/Look: 56-57; /Vladimir Zakharov: 22-23

NASA: 66-67

Shutterstock: 8-9, 10-11, 12-13, 14-15, 16-17, 24-25, 26-27, 30-31, 42-43, 46-47, 50-51, 54-55,
58-59, 62-63, 64-65, 72-73, 74-75, 76-77, 84-87

Every effort has been made to acknowledge correctly and contact the source and/or copyright
holder of each picture and Carlton Books Limited apologizes for any unintentional errors or
omissions, which will be corrected in future editions of this book.

Project editor: Matthew Lowing
Puzzle creator: Danny Baldwin

EXTREME
SPOT THE DIFFERENCE
CHALLENGING HIGH-DEFINITION PHOTO PUZZLES

CARLTON
BOOKS

CONTENTS

INTRODUCTION

You hold in your hands a book that is something a little special. Quite apart from anything else, it holds a fascinating selection of beautiful images. These range from the mechanical to the natural, from the ancient to the modern – and all of them dazzling. But the main attraction is the thrilling selection of puzzles that the pictures represent – hours of captivating entertainment and mental exercise.

Humans are very visual creatures. We make sense of the world with our eyes. That's why people love 'Spot the Difference' puzzles so much. They dovetail naturally with the way that our brains actually work, in a manner that abstract mathematical puzzles do not. It gives us pleasure to look at a fresh, beautiful scene, and to get a good mental understanding of it. The more detail there is, the more that's there to hold our interest. **Extreme Spot the Difference** offers an amazing range of gorgeous, finely detailed images to delight the eye of course, but it also provides something better – a chance for the brain to really exercise its visual comparison circuitry. We know that the alterations are there, that the two sights are not actually identical. It's all down to the brain's capability to assess, categorize, compare and analyze.

You see, beating puzzles is not just about finding the answer. If it was, puzzle books would be incredibly easy. The important part is the challenge. **Extreme Spot the Difference** aims squarely at the trickier end of the spectrum; completing the book is a significant achievement. And that's what's important.

Humans love puzzles. They're part of the experience of being the people that we are. Every culture we know of, both across the world and down through history, has engaged in puzzles of one form or another. We have a drive to learn and understand, and puzzles provide us with a fantastic way of engaging that drive in a setting that can provide a meaningful task, but where the possible consequences of failure are low. If you fail at a puzzle, you can always try again.

Part of the appeal of puzzles is undoubtedly the urge that we all have to rank and compare ourselves. We have a natural inclination to order ourselves within a group of people – before him, after her, and so on. Status is a complicated thing, but it's part of the human group dynamic. But our competitive tendencies are not just directed outwards. We also long to excel, to compete with our own past selves and demonstrate progress and improvement. The urge to be the best that you can be is behind much of humanity's progress over the last 200,000 years. Puzzles offer a great chance to get an idea of performance in that regard. Hard puzzles in particular offer a unique opportunity – a real challenge, with a meaningful achievement in beating them.

That challenge is in fact its own reward however, for there is another vital function that puzzles hold – that of mental exercise. The maxim "use it or lose it" is well known from the sphere of physical pursuits. If you never stretch a muscle, it shrinks, because the body decides that as you never need to use it much, it doesn't have to be as strong. The same principle applies to the brain. If you never stretch your mental muscles, they atrophy. The scientific term for this is 'brain plasticity'. The mental circuits that you exercise get strengthened, built up in order to make the process easier and more efficient. At the same time, circuits you ignore are shrunk, because they're just not very useful. In other words, your brain adapts, in exactly the same way that your body does, to the life that you lead. You become ever more finely tuned for doing the things that you do habitually. Unfortunately, that means that if you just sit around watching TV, your mental muscles become weak and flabby. Doing puzzles gives your mind the chance to work itself, strengthening your intellectual capabilities.

As medical science continues to grant us longer and longer average lifespans, puzzles will get ever-more important as a vital weapon in the fight for a happy, productive, enjoyable life.

The weapon you now hold is particularly potent. I'm sure you'll enjoy it.

HOW TO PLAY

Extreme Spot the Difference wouldn't be very extreme if the puzzles were easy. So don't make the mistake of thinking that this is going to be a gentle stroll in the park. There are 38 puzzles in the book; the first 36 have 50 differences to find and the last two an incredible 100 changes!

The picture puzzles changes are an entertaining mix of the obvious (once you have seen them that is), ingenious and the downright devious. As well as being a supreme test of your observation skills, we are confident that you will find this book lots of fun and it will keep you occupied for hours, days, weeks and perhaps even months!

With 2,000 extreme differences to find, you are going to have your work cut out as you attempt to identify all of the changes, so here are a few handy hints and tips to help you on your way.

Before you begin, have a pen and some paper to hand so you can write down the coordinates of the devious differences as and when you find them. You can later compare these to the answers section found at the back of the book. For each of the puzzles, the pink coordinate's axis is noted first, followed by blue. The original unaltered photograph is shown first and is followed by the changed version.

To help you in your hunt, we've included with the book a unique aid for you – the plastic **Spotter's Grid**. Place it over the picture to help isolate a small section, which you can then easily compare with its near twin on the other page.

Armed with your **Spotter's Grid** and your powers of observation, all that is left to say is best of luck and happy hunting!

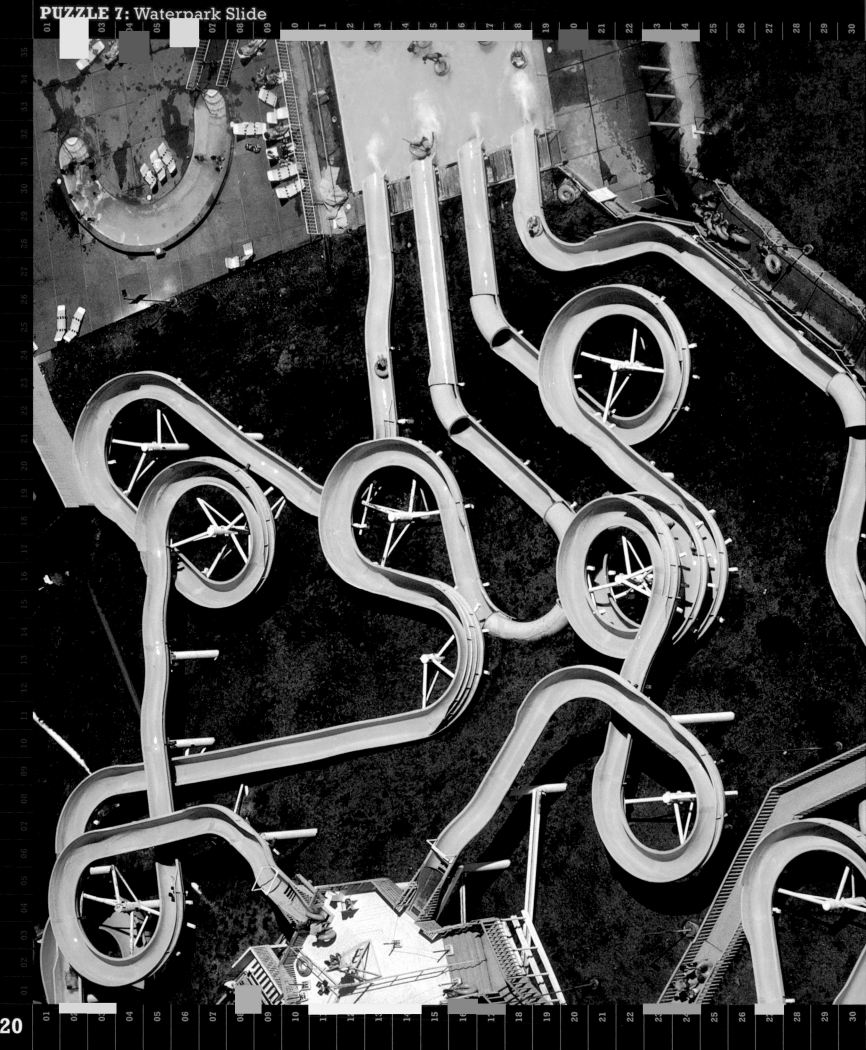

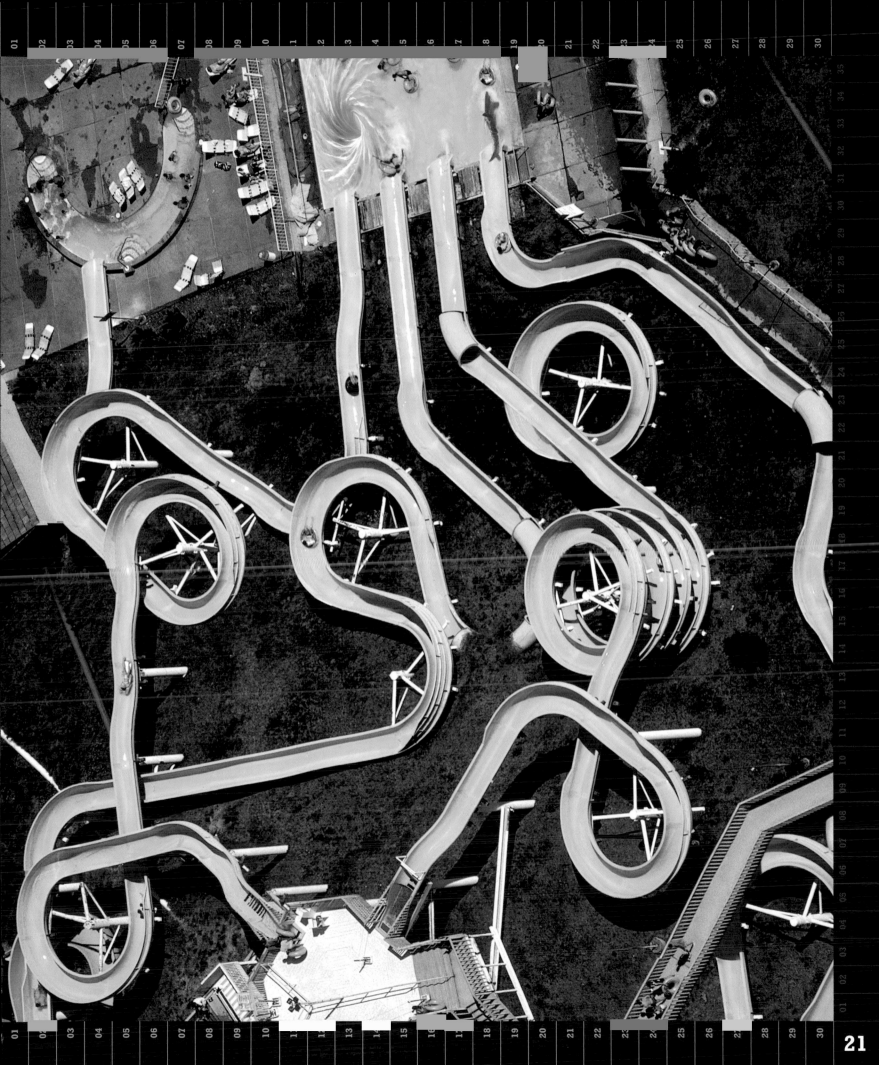

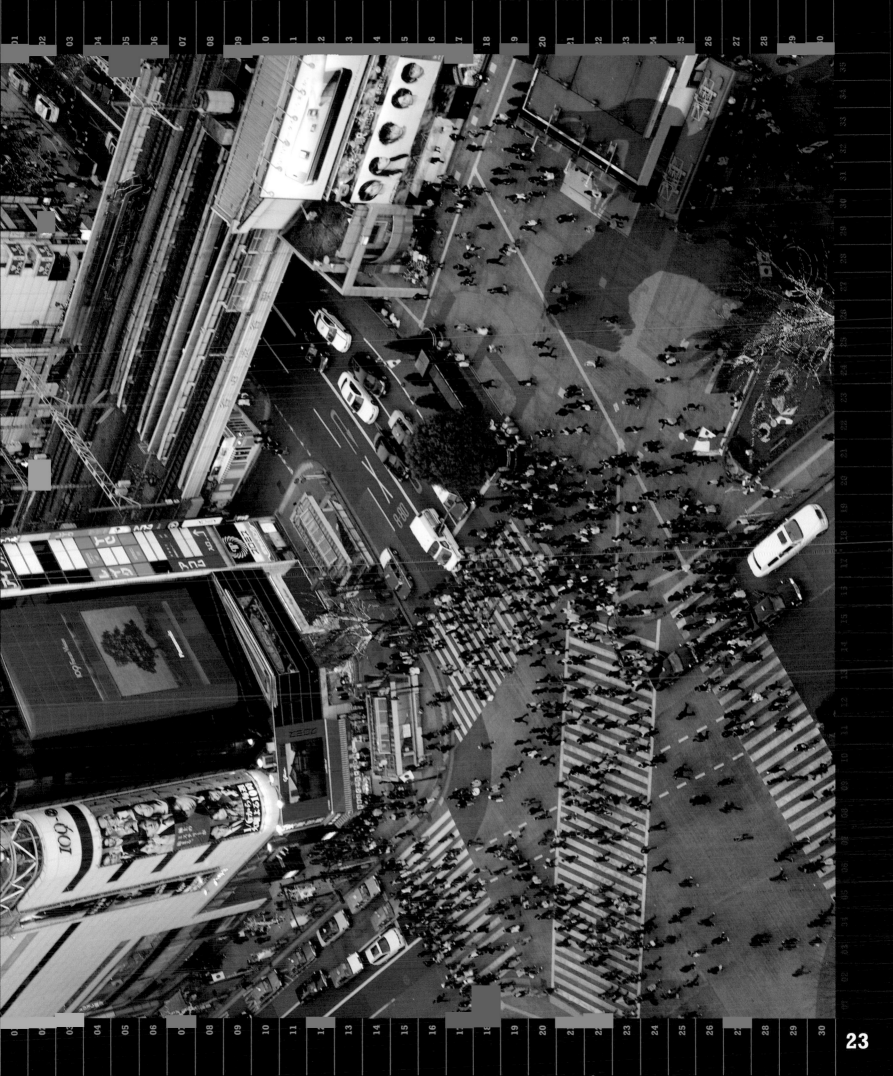

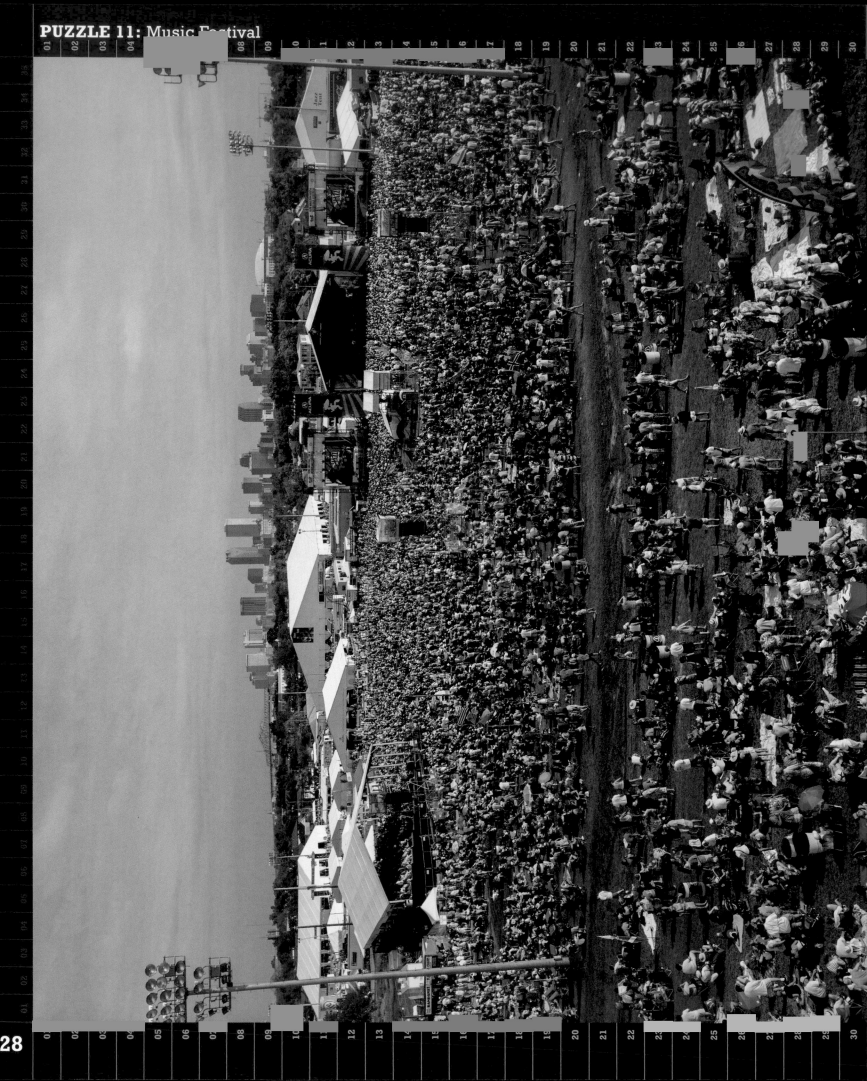

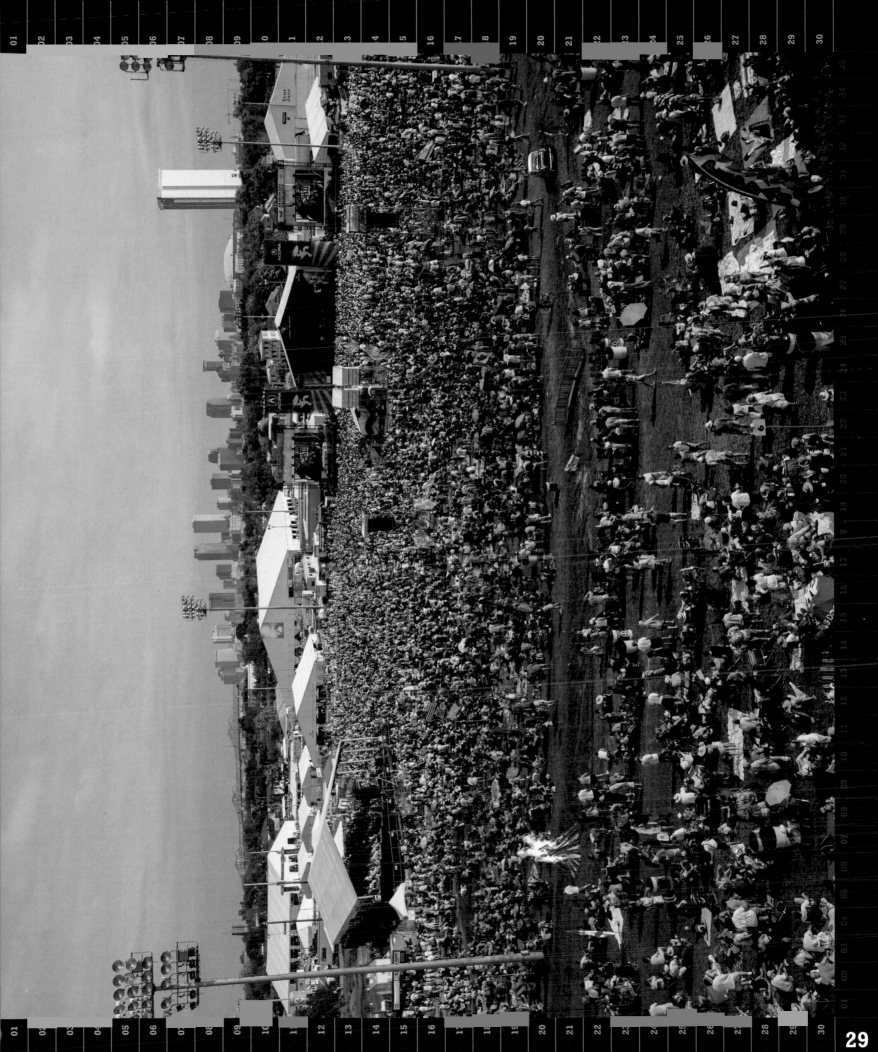

29

35

36

47

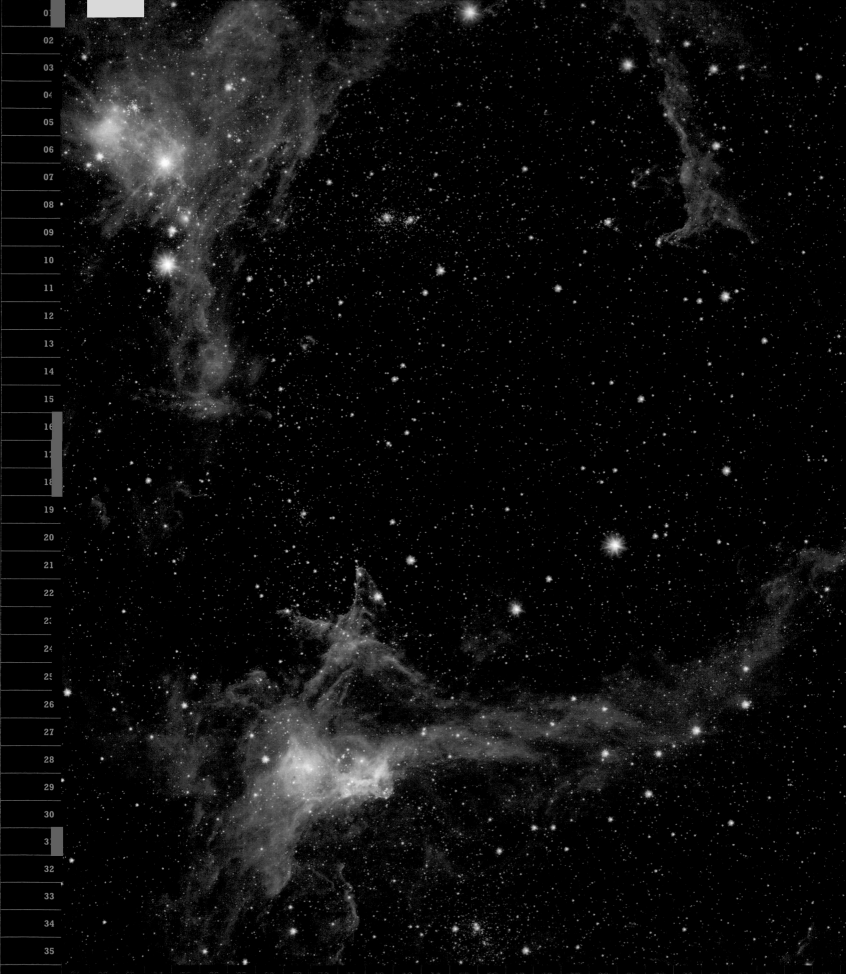

69

ANSWERS

Puzzle 1: Manhattan (page 08)

01-02	03	Added: Helicopter
01-02	26-28	Added: Height to tower
01-02	31-32	Changed: Window – yellow to blue
02	09-10	Changed: Statue of Liberty enlarged
02-03	17-18	Added: Light in window
03-05	10-11	Added: Ocean liner
05-06	26-27	Added: Rooftop swimming pool
06-07	10	Added: Lights
06-07	18-21	Added: Building extension
08-09	08-10	Added: Building
08-09	23-33	Changed: Building extended
09-13	11-12	Added: Bridge
0?	34	Added: Neon sign
13-15	05-08	Added: Extra floor
13-15	09-10	Added: Extra floor
15-20	16-17	Removed: Roof structures
16-18	19-20	Added: Roof unit
17	34	Added: Window
17-18	18	Added: Light to window
17-23	03-07	Added: Fireworks
18-19	13-14	Added: Gorilla
19-20	09-10	Changed: Light – pink to green
20-21	20	Added: Smoke
20-22	12-13	Changed: Building
20-30	05-07	Added: Clouds
21-22	16-19	Added: Metal framework
21-23	08-09	Added: Mountain
22	10	Added: Building
22-23	18-20	Changed: Building buttress
23	31	Added: Light to window
24	01-04	Changed: Building point extended
24	05	Added: Satellite dishes
24	33	Changed: Lights – yellow to blue
24-25	18-19	Changed: Window darkened
24-25	20-21	Added: Building strip pattern extended
25-26	15	Added: Peak
25-?	15-16	Added: Building extended
2?	2-13	Added: Building wing
26-27	22-35	Changed: Building strip – pink-grey to yellow
27-28	11	Removed: Building
27-28	34	Removed: Building light
27-29	11-14	Added: Building
27-29	16-19	Added: Building with clock
28-29	27-28	Added: Window
28	22-23	Added: Man on roof
28-29	08	Added: UFO
29	30	Added: Window
29-30	22-23	Added: Satellite dish
30	16-19	Added: Tower
30	19-20	Removed: Red light

Puzzle 2: Container Port (page 10)

01	21	Added: Box
01	28	Removed: Man
01-02	08	Added: "70t"
01-02	18-19	Added: Layers of palettes
01-02	19-20	Changed: Base of crane extended
01-12	28-35	Added: Cable
02-04	34-35	Added: Dolphin
04-06	11	Added: Two green containers
04-05	26-26	Added: White marking on truck
04-06	19	Removed: Street markings
05-06	14	Added: Layer of containers
05-08	09-10	Changed: Crane marking – white to red
06-07	11-17	Added: Lamppost
07-08	23-24	Removed: Truck cab
08	20-21	Removed: "4"
08	25	Added: Two black bollards
09-10	16-17	Changed: Container – orange to blue
09-10	20-21	Changed: Container – yellow to orange
09-11	23-26	Changed: Stripe – red to yellow
10-11	15-17	Changed: Crane leg – white to red
10-11	25	Removed: Chain
12-13	09-10	Removed: Platform steps
12-13	25	Added: Unit to wall
13-14	10-11	Changed: Crane leg moved to front
13-14	23-24	Removed: Diagonal strut from mast
14-15	14-18	Added: Length to mast
14-15	32-34	Removed: White markings
14-16	31-33	Added: Anchor
15-16	20-21	Changed: Container – white to yellow
15-17	14-15	Added: Red container
16	25-26	Added: Door
16-17	07	Added: Two more units
16-17	27-28	Changed: Small platform enlarged
17	26	Removed: Red object
17-18	09-10	Added: "70t"
17-18	32-35	Added: Iceberg
18-19	03-08	Removed: Crane leg
19-21	14-15	Changed: Container – red to yellow
20-21	15-16	Added: Floating container
22-23	12-13	Changed: Length to crane leg
23	26-27	Removed: Ship fixture
25-26	12-13	Removed: Orange container
25-26	13-14	Changed: Container – blue to white
25-27	19-21	Added: Container
25-30	11	Changed: Bar – red to yellow
26	13	Removed: Window
27-28	05	Removed: Top of crane
27-29	20-21	Removed: Top of metal framework
29-30	12	Added: Object placed on container
29-30	28-29	Added: Container

Puzzle 3: Clockworks (page 12)

01-02	15	Added: One bolt
01-02	22-23	Changed: Roundel (now decorative)
01-02	35	Added: Curved metal
01-04	24-26	Removed: Shadow
01-03	06-12	Changed: Metal rusted
02-04	32-34	Removed: Cog
04-05	18-19	Changed: Screwhead
04-07	01-04	Added: Brass arrow
05-06	10-17	Removed: Rusty bar
06-07	18-19	Added: Engraving
06-10	22-30	Added: Smoke
07-08	32-33	Added: Spring
11-14	15-22	Added: Spiderweb
12	03-05	Removed: Engraving
12-13	28-29	Changed: Screwhead
13-14	32-33	Changed: Screwhead – grey to orange
13-15	22-23	Changed: Cog now visible
13-19	32-35	Removed: Cog
14-15	09-10	Removed: Hole
14-15	24-25	Changed: Size of screw reduced
14-16	05-06	Added: Metal bar
15	19	Added: Screw
17	04-05	Added: Screw with lever
17-18	28-30	Removed: Screw
17-19	32-33	Changed: Screw and shadow reversed
18-20	26-28	Changed: Engraved lettering
18-23	21-26	Added: Cog
19-20	07-08	Added: Knob
19-20	13-14	Added: Rivet
20	31-32	Changed: Letter – R to A
21-22	11	Added: Screw
21-24	01-02	Added: Water droplets
22-23	07-08	Added: Engraved numbers
22-26	21-22	Added: Metal lever
23-24	16-17	Changed: Bolt – gold to red
23-24	35	Added: Roundel
23-25	13-14	Changed: Screw reduced
24-26	27-29	Added: Brass arrow
24-25	08-10	Changed: Round item
25-26	02-05	Changed: Colour – orange to grey
25-26	01-02	Changed: Brass circle filled
25-27	32-35	Changed: Surface now pitted
26-27	08-10	Added: Mouse
25-30	20-21	Added: Metal bar with screws
26-30	28-31	Added: Lever
27-28	16-17	Added: Spider
27-29	10-14	Changed: Cog – gold to silver
27-30	34-35	Added: Cog
28-30	24-26	Added: Cogs
30	27	Added: Bolt

Puzzle 4: Boston (page 14)

02	20	Added: Satellite dish
03-04	16	Removed: Roof box
03-04	22-23	Removed: Roof unit
03-04	27-28	Changed: Window
04-06	09-12	Removed: Floor
07-08	22-23	Added: Skylight extended
07-08	25-26	Removed: Window
07-10	24	Added: Wall
07-08	07-09	Added: Tree
08-10	08-10	Changed: Rooftop flipped
08-10	25-26	Added: Balcony
10-13	20	Added: Fence
11-12	15	Added: Chimney
12-13	02-04	Removed: Path under trees
13-16	13-15	Changed: Tree – green to red
13	21-22	Added: Statue
16	04-05	Added: Barbecue
16	16-17	Added: Skier
16	27-28	Changed: Window
11-12	20-21	Removed: Skylight
17-19	24-26	Changed: Building front
20-21	10-11	Added: Ventilation unit
20-21	16-17	Changed: Skylight extended
21-22	04-06	Added: Extra storey
21-22	08-09	Added: Fire escape stairs
22-23	19-20	Added: Roof unit
23-24	07	Changed: Roof
23-24	09-10	Added: Roof skylight
23-24	23-24	Removed: Air-conditioning unit
23-24	15-17	Added: Tennis court
24-27	01-02	Added: Fire and smoke
25	02-03	Removed: Window
25-26	05	Added: Helicopter pad
25-27	23	Changed: Awning – blue to orange
28	16-18	Added: Chimney extended
29	16-17	Added: Chimney
29	11-12	Changed: Window
29-30	26-27	Added: Window curtain
29-31	19-20	Added: Tree
31	22-23	Added: Chairs and tables
31-32	17-18	Added: Roof unit
31	23	Removed: Skylight
31-33	04-05	Added: Garden umbrella
32	24	Removed: Window
33-34	08-09	Added: Roof shed

Removed: Pyramid roof
Removed: Chimney
Removed: Window
Added: Tent
Added: Window

Puzzle 5:
Amusement Park (page 16)

Added: Umbrella
Changed: Red bar to white balustrade
Added: Sign
Removed: White support
Changed: Colour of decoration
Removed: Ferris wheel car
Removed: Netting
Removed: Support
Changed: Picture on carousel
Changed: Pink elephant reversed
Removed: Metal post
Changed: Box outline – yellow to blue
Changed: Shell – green to orange
Changed: Pillar – yellow to purple
Added: Top hat
Removed: Platform
Removed: Painted decoration
Added: Person on stairs
Changed: "M" to "C"
Changed: Sign – "exit" to "enter"
Changed: Sign frame – blue to purple
Added: Height to rollercoaster
Removed: Fence post
Changed: Umbrella – orange to pink
Changed: Support – white to orange
Added: Dustbin
Removed: Sign
Changed: Stripes – blue to pink
Changed: Centre of ferris wheel
Changed: Stripe – yellow to blue
Changed: "4" to "5"
Changed: Cigarette to clown
Added: Teddy bears
Changed: "R" to "L"
Removed: Spoke of ferris wheel
Changed: Sign – "exit" to "enter"
Removed: Post
Added: Bungee jumper
Removed: Guitar
Removed: Green support
Added: Umbrella
Changed: Stripes – orange to blue
Removed: Rowing boat from picture
Removed: No smoking sign
Added: Pattern to roofing edge
Removed: Sign
Added: "Exit" sign
Changed: Decoration – orange to blue
Added: White sphere to "crown"
Changed: Ferris wheel car – red to blue

Puzzle 6:
Rio de Janeiro (page 18)

Added: Steps
Removed: Carport roof
Added: Half-built room
Removed: Window
Changed: Canvas – blue to green
Added: People on roof
Added: Tree
Added: Fence
Changed: Wall – purple to blue
Added: Roof
Added: Washing line
Added: Window
Changed: Roofing materials
Removed: Washing line
Added: Car on roof
Added: Covered walkway
Changed: Distortion to building
Added: Blue container

Added: Water container
Added: Waterfall
Added: Fire in window
Added: Basketball hoop
Changed: Surface on terrace
Removed: Water container
Changed: Building – grey to yellow
Removed: Hanging sheets
Changed: Wall – red to purple
Added: New storey to building
Added: Loud speaker system
Added: Satellite dish
Changed: Top floor of building
Changed: Wall – red to purple
Added: New storey to building
Added: Terrace
Changed: Building roof top
Removed: Hanging clothes
Removed: Word on wall
Changed: Bigger window
Added: Wall surface and window
Removed: Wall colour
Added: Extra steps
Changed: Wall – yellow to red
Added: Hanging sheet
Added: Window
Changed: Sheet – white to blue
Changed: Car – yellow to blue
Added: Logo to van
Added: Tree
Added: New storey to building
Added: Road sign

Puzzle 7:
Waterpark Slide (page 20)

Added: Sign
Removed: Post
Changed: Stripes – black to blue
Removed: Lifeguard on chair
Removed: Strut
Removed: Yellow ring
Removed: Rope support and shadow
Removed: Shadow
Added: Man
Removed: Strut
Changed: Pathway over flume
Changed: Mat – orange to blue
Removed: White bars
Added: Stripes
Added: White support
Removed: Flume support
Added: Struts
Removed: Dark stain
Added: Woman on slide
Changed: Route of flume, layer added
Added: Grass and dirt over tunnel
Removed: Shadow
Removed: Pipes and infrastructure
Added: Person in yellow ring
Added: Roof
Removed: Tunnel
Added: Tree
Changed: Ring – yellow to black
Added: Slide
Removed: Fence rail
Changed: Recliners – blue to pink
Added: Water stain on ground
Added: Reclining chair
Removed: Person with ring
Added: Red and white dustbin
Added: Steps
Added: Signpost
Added: Man sitting
Removed: Rings
Added: Pole
Changed: pool cover – blue to red
Added: Whirlpool
Added: Pipe
Added: Person in Pool
Added: Shark

Added: Yellow ring
Added: Person with rings
Added: Ring
Removed: Fence
Added: Sign

Puzzle 8:
Rush Hour (page 22)

Removed: Man on bicycle
Changed: Car – green to orange
Removed: Tree with lights
Removed: Pedestrian crossing stripe
Changed: Wall – brown to grey
Added: Light
Removed: Road circle
Removed: Manhole cover
Added: Pedestrian
Changed: Poster – orange to purple
Removed: Pedestrian
Added: Canopy pattern
Added: Sign
Added: Pedestrian
Removed: Pedestrian
Added: Wall
Changed: Neon sign – orange to purple
Removed: Car reflection
Removed: Neon sign
Changed: Direction of stairs
Changed: Car length
Added: Green panel
Added: Extra triangular skylight
Changed: Road markings – "2" to "8"
Removed: Road markings
Removed: Road markings
Changed: Road marking – orange to white
Added: Unit
Removed: Red dot
Added: Tree branch
Changed: Building extended
Added: Yellow cable end
Added: Bridge marking
Removed: Flag
Added: Train
Added: Godzilla shadow
Added: Fence post
Added: Metallic bin
Removed: Road cone
Removed: Sign
Removed: Car
Added: Pillar
Added: Blue advert to balcony
Removed: Roof unit
Changed: Poster head
Removed: Yellow line
Added: White square
Added: Height to fixture
Added: Fixture to tram roof
Added: Tree

Puzzle 9:
Amphitheatre (page 24)

Added: Boat
Added: Car
Removed: Car
Added: Lighting stand
Added: Two people
Removed: Object from stage
Changed: Stage enlarged
Added: Height to pillar
Added: Length to stonework
Changed: New blocks to old
Added: Stone decoration
Removed: Window
Changed: Flat rooftop extended
Added: Row of seats
Added: Whale
Added: Satellite dish
Added: Tree
Added: Train

13	10	Added: Car
15	19–20	Added: Lion
15–16	34–35	Removed: Rooftop window
16–17	02–03	Changed: Building extended
16–17	03–04	Removed: Building
16–18	07–08	Changed: Wall – pink to green
17–19	28–30	Removed: Zebra Crossing
19	01	Removed: Building with domed roof
19	12	Removed: Window
19–24	04–05	Added: Two storeys to building
20	10–11	Added: Circular tower to rooftop
20–21	09	Removed: Lamp post
20–21	13–14	Changed: Umbrella – green to red
20–21	24–25	Removed: Steps
21–22	10	Removed: Stonework from roof
22–25	11–12	Changed: Surface of rooftop
22	12–13	Removed: Stonework
22–23	17–18	Added: Extra steps
22–23	31	Removed: Car
23	12	Added: Window
23–24	29	Added: Window shutters
24–25	27	Removed: Skylight
25	24	Added: Dirt to truck
26–27	09–10	Changed: Wall – orange to grey
27	31–32	Removed: Chimney
27–29	13	Changed: Wall – yellow to grey
28–29	09–10	Changed: Wall – yellow to blue
28–29	17	Changed: Car – pink to yellow
28–29	25	Changed: Chimney enlarged
28–30	10–11	Added: Tree
29	01–02	Added: Building with red roof
29	08	Added: Tree

Puzzle 10:
Floating Market (page 26)

01	32–33	Removed: Bottle
01–07	10–11	Changed: Roof – blue to red
03–04	14–15	Removed: Straw hat
04	11–12	Removed: Steel bar
06–07	02	Changed: Umbrella – green to yellow
06–07	19–20	Added: Basket
07–08	16	Changed: Red fruit to apples
07–09	25–26	Removed: Rope
08–09	15–16	Added: Pineapple
09–10	10	Added: Duck
12–13	03–04	Changed: Umbrella – green to red
12–13	04–06	Added: Figure carrying baskets
12–14	24–25	Added: Bundle
12–14	29–30	Added: Fish
13–14	04	Removed: Lantern
15–16	15–16	Changed: Container – pink to green
15–17	27–28	Changed: Card – blue to grey
15–16	02–04	Removed: Pink decoration
16–17	09–13	Removed: Wooden pole
16–17	13–14	Added: Straw hat
17	15	Added: Fruit to container
18	02–04	Added: Hanging flowers
18–19	05–06	Removed: Wooden post
18–19	21–22	Changed: Basket – blue to orange
18–19	30–31	Removed: Apron straps from back
19	03	Added: Hat
19	06–10	Removed: Umbrella
20–21	12–13	Changed: Hat
20–21	13	Changed: Towel – pink to blue
20–21	22	Removed: Inlaid decoration
21–22	08–09	Added: Figure on boat
21–22	19–20	Removed: Lid from pot
21–22	23–24	Added: Bananas
23	04–05	Added: Rope
23–24	14–16	Changed: Gas tank – green to red
23–28	06–07	Changed: Boat hull – blue to red
24–25	04–06	Added: Figure on boat
24–25	32–33	Added: Layer of containers to tray
24–25	11–13	Changed: Shirt – grey to red
25–26	10–11	Changed: Flowers – yellow to red
25–26	27	Added: Bowl of dumplings
25–26	02	Changed: Roof – no longer rusting
28–30	07–08	Added: Person in canoe
26–28	33–35	Added: Fish
29	08–11	Added: Umbrella

29–30	05–06	Added: Dog
29–30	06	Removed: Words from boat
29–30	14–15	Apron straps – red to purple
29–30	16	Added: Rice to bowl
30	03	Added: Lantern

Puzzle 11:
Music Festival (page 28)

01–02	15	Removed: Wording on banner
02–03	24–25	Changed: Large man slimmed down
03	06–08	Added: Another light to rig
03	20	Removed: Metal plate
03–04	21–23	Changed: Colour of banner
04	09	Added: Height to church
05	24	Changed: Dress – pink to turquoise
05–10	09	Added: Cable supports bridge
06–07	19–21	Added: Bonfire
07–08	23–25	Changed: Two men reversed
08–09	13	Changed: Box on scaffolding reversed
08–09	28–29	Changed: Umbrella – red to blue
11–13	17	Changed: Flag – orange to blue
13–14	20–21	Removed: Man
14–15	10–11	Changed: Poster
15–16	07–12	Added: Lighting rig
15–16	18–20	Added: Banner
15–16	29–30	Changed: Umbrella – blue to pink
17–19	25–26	Changed: Chair to children's buggy
18–19	13–14	Removed: Box on scaffolding
19	21–22	Removed: Woman
19–20	20–21	Added: Dustbin
19–21	12–14	Removed: Black diagonal pole removed
20–21	09–10	Removed: Building roof
20–21	21–22	Added: Flag
20–22	10–11	Changed: Banner – yellow to blue
21	26–27	Added: Shirt to man's back
22–23	24–25	Removed: Person
22	27–28	Changed: "6" to "9"
22–25	20–21	Added: Wooden bridge
23	10	Changed: Logo enlarged
23	13	Added: White cover to stand
24	08	Added: Height to tower
24–25	10	Added: Height to building
24–25	18	Changed: Flag – Norway to Canada
25–26	11	Changed: Stage decoration reversed
26	23–24	Added: Umbrella
26–27	19–20	Changed: Woman to a man on bicycle
27	24	Changed: Chair – blue to pink
28–29	23–25	Added: Man walking
30–31	06–09	Added: Building
30–31	25	Removed: White sheet
31–32	20	Added: Car
32–33	20–21	Changed: Woman reversed
32–33	22–23	Added: One person sitting on blue rug
32–34	26–27	Changed: Rug – green to yellow
33–35	11–12	Removed: Coca cola trucks
34	11	Changed: 'Jazz Tent' to "Tent Jazz"
35	06–07	Removed: Light and rigging
35	13	Changed: Portaloo – purple to green

Puzzle 12:
Church Basilica (page 30)

01–02	27–28	Added: Sheet of paper
02	15–16	Changed: Gown – red to blue
02–03	10–11	Removed: Box
04	19–20	Removed: Cross (but not its shadow)
04–05	11–12	Changed: Decoration on light
04–05	13–14	Added: Dove
04–05	17–19	Changed: Column extended
04–05	32	Removed: Red book
05–06	13–14	Changed: Ceiling – blue to mustard
08–09	20–22	Added: Picture in gold frame
10	23–24	Added: Statue
12	15–18	Added: Light suspended from chain
12	18–19	Changed: 7 pillars to 3
12	23	Added: Chair
12–13	20–22	Changed: Banner – green to red
12–13	22–23	Removed: Top of pulpit
13	14	Changed: Part of ceiling – gold to blue
13–15	13–14	Changed: Ceiling – blue to mustard

14	21–23	Added: Pillar
13–14	22–23	Removed: Triangular item
14–16	19–20	Changed: Ceiling design to stained-glass window
14–16	23	Added: Trim decoration
15	08–09	Added: Boss to ceiling
15	22–23	Changed: Image on altar piece
15	23–24	Removed: Image on altar
15–16	17–18	Changed: Figures reversed
15–18	30–33	Added: Spilt chalice
16	02	Removed: Star
16	23–24	Added: Plant
16–17	07–08	Changed: Cherub reversed
19	01–02	Changed: Halo
19	16–17	Removed: Fixtures
19	22–23	Removed: Display board
20	22–23	Added: Banner
20–21	06–08	Changed: Ceiling – blue to green
20–22	13–22	Added: Beam of light
22	02–07	Removed: Window
22	23	Removed: Wooden base of pillar
22–23	07–09	Removed: Wall painting
22–23	16–18	Removed: Wall painting
22–23	30–35	Removed: Carving on pew
23–24	02–04	Added: Angel
24–30	23–24	Removed: Wooden panelling
24–30	33–35	Removed: Pew
25–26	27–28	Removed: Wooden support
26	02–08	Removed: Light chain
26	17–18	Removed: Wall column decoration
27	11	Added: Electrical unit to box
28	20–21	Removed: Purple reflected light
28	07–09	Added: Gold carving

Puzzle 13:
Formula 1 Pitstop (page 32)

03–04	08–09	Added: Metal loop
04–05	23	Added: Stain on ground
05	30–35	Removed: Line in concrete
05–06	06–07	Added: Two black cables
06–07	05–06	Changed: Sneaker
07–09	05–06	Changed: Patch reversed
08–09	33–35	Changed: Hat
10–14	20–26	Added: Person
11–12	11–12	Added: Spanner
12–14	01–03	Removed: Textured ground surface
13	28	Changed: Logo reversed
13–14	13	Removed: Stripes
15	11–14	Added: Bicycle pump
15	15	Removed: Wing mirror
15–16	27–28	Added: Another strut to suspension
15–16	33–35	Removed: Leg
16	04–05	Removed: Metal item
16	31	Changed: Letter "d" to "n"
16–17	07	Removed: White lettering
16–17	07–08	Changed: Logo
16–17	08–09	Changed: "9" to "6"
16–18	14–16	Added: Windscreen
16–18	17–18	Changed: Helmet – yellow to blue
17	01–03	Added: Metal pole
17	10–11	Added: White logo
17	16–17	Added: PlayStation console
17	19–20	Added: Yellow bar
17	24	Changed: Logo – horse to cat
17	26	Changed: "FIAT" to "FATI"
17–18	03–04	Removed: metal wings
17–18	13	Added: Yellow triangle
18	20–21	Changed: Letter "E" to "A"
18–19	23–24	Added: Vents
19–23	30–35	Added: Black cables
20	30–32	Added: Flame to exhaust
20–21	01–02	Changed: Sign – red to black
20–21	05–06	Changed: Drill to a banana
21–22	20–21	Added: Red sneaker
21–23	08–10	Changed: Tread on tyre
22–23	03–04	Changed: Patch reversed
23–24	22	Added: Orange road marking
23–24	30–31	Changed: Helmet reversed
23–30	16	Added: Crack
24–25	02	Changed: Tool – red to yellow
26–27	31–32	Added: Magnifying glass

26-23	11-12	Added: Leg
		Removed: Stripes
	08	Added: Dollar bill
28-29	07-08	Changed: Handle – blue to red
28-29	32	Added: Tarantula

Puzzle 14: Grand Bazaar (page 34)

01-03	20-23	Changed: Shirt – green to red
03-04	10-12	Changed: Material – orange to pink
03-04	22-23	Removed: Beard
06	16-17	Removed: Sandals
08	08	Removed: Number "1"
10	17-18	Changed: Man's head
10-12	19-20	Added: Headscarf
11-12	17	Added: Hat
1?	03-04	Changed: Letter "E" to "A"
12-13	10	Removed: Golden decoration
12-13	10-12	Changed: Sign colour – red to blue
13-14	08	Changed: Sign colour – red to blue
13-17	29-30	Added: Manhole cover
14-15	17-19	Changed: Cardigan – yellow to red
15	10	Added: Security camera
16	22-24	Removed: Shoe box
16-17	06	Changed: Sign lettering
16-17	1?	Removed: Fixture
16-17	16	Removed: Shop mannequin
17	11-12	Changed: Sign edge – orange to blue
17	13	Added: Light
17	13-14	Removed: Lamp
1?	15-16	Added: Male figure
1?	14-15	Changed: Letter "E" to "Z"
1?	11-12	Changed: Sign logo
18-19	16-17	Added: Hat
18-19	19	Added: Sunglasses
1?	13	Removed: Light
19-20	09	Removed: Light bulb
19-33	02-04	Removed: Electrical wire
20-21	06-07	Changed: Head flipped
2?	01-02	Removed: Plant
2?	19-22	Changed: Length and colour of hair
2?	14-15	Added: Coat
22-23	01-02	Changed: Window moulding
23	03-05	Removed: Moulded decoration
23	11-12	Removed: Metal hook
23-24	10	Added: Light
23-24	10	Added: Lamp
23-25	17-20	Removed: Man
23-25	28-29	Removed: Bag
25-26	01-03	Changed: Direction of wall stripes
25-27	20-22	Changed: Woman's head reversed
29-30	16-17	Changed: Sign – orange to turquoise
29-30	01-04	Added: Sign
3?	14	Added: Extra orange
31-32	17-18	Removed: Grille
31-33	19-21	Added: Bag
33-34	12-13	Removed: Pole decoration
33-34	23-25	Removed: Number "3"

Puzzle 15: Station Market (page 36)

01-02	14-15	Removed: Rock
03-04	18-19	Added: Chicken
03-04	24-26	Changed: Material – green to red
03-05	10-12	Changed: Windows reversed
04-05	25-26	Added: Red turban
06-07	25	Changed: Oranges to apples
09-10	27-30	Added: Woman
0?	20-22	Added: Blue pole
0?	15	Added: Basket
0?	02-03	Added: Window
09-10	29-32	Changed: Sari – brown to purple
10-12	11-12	Added: Pig
10-12	19-24	Added: Man
11-16	01-03	Changed: Wall
	24-26	Removed: Bag
14?	15-18	Changed: Shirt – colours
16	02-03	Removed: Drainpipe

16-17	23-26	Changed: Rucksack – red to blue
16-18	08-09	Added: Bundle
16-18	13-15	Added: Man with flowers
18	02	Added: Snake
18	21-22	Removed: Writing on bag
18	29-31	Added: Bundle
18-19	18	Added: Baseball cap
18-19	23-27	Added: Woman
20	03-04	Removed: Sign on post
20-21	08	Added: Basket
20-21	33-35	Removed: Bundle
20-22	09-10	Added: Striped tarpaulin
21-22	13-14	Changed: Man now carries flowers
21-22	15-16	Added: Headscarf
21-23	16-17	Added: Rice
21-24	23-26	Changed: Shirt – colours of stripes
22-23	06-07	Removed: Stripey material
22-23	25	Removed: Hat
22-23	22-24	Changed: Singlet – white to black
22-24	01-02	Changed: Wall – green to pink
22-24	13-14	Added: White bundle
23	12-13	Added: Green shawl on man
24-25	11-12	Added: Basket
24-26	19-22	Changed: Man now reversed
24-27	33-35	Added: Man in brown striped shirt
26	02	Removed: Item on roof
26-27	25-27	Changed: Shirt – checks to plain
27-30	11-12	Changed: Bundle – orange to white
28	01	Added: Sign
28-29	15	Changed: Pattern on sweater
28-30	18-25	Added: Tarpaulin
29	03-04	Removed: People from doorframe
29	09-10	Added: Giant corn

Puzzle 16: Bondi Beach (page 38)

01-02	23-24	Changed: Shorts – blue to crimson
01-04	08-09	Removed: Sun shade
03	16-17	Added: Bucket
03-04	07-08	Changed: Building – blue to green
04-06	14	Removed: Towels and basket
05-09	30-34	Changed: Woman now suntanned
06	17-18	Removed: Woman in striped top
07-08	09	Removed: Gazebo
09-12	17-18	Removed: Figures lying face down
11	13	Changed: Parasol segments – blue to white
12	05-06	Added: Tree
12	22	Removed: Watermelon
12-13	24	Changed: Bikini – yellow to pink
12-14	15-16	Added: Girl reading magazine
13	17-18	Added: Tattoo on man's back
14-15	24-26	Changed: Shirt stripes – blue to green
15	20	Removed: Blue cap
15-16	06	Added: House
15-16	13-14	Added: Green parasol
16	08	Added: Sign
16	10	Changed: Tent – yellow to blue
16	16-17	Added: Straw hat
16-18	22-23	Changed: chiller – blue to brown
17-18	15-16	Added: Person sitting in chair
19	11-12	Removed: Beach buggy
19-20	07	Added: Storey to building
20	14-15	Changed: Bikini to swimming costume
21	06-09	Added: Lamp post
21-24	09	Changed: Wall painted
21-24	26-27	Changed: Surfboard – blue to red
21-27	29-32	Added: Sandcastle
22	12-13	Removed: Two figures
22-23	04-05	Added: Tower
22-23	14	Removed: Woman's bikini bottom
22-24	08-09	Changed: Beach scene on billboard
23	15-17	Added: Man
24-25	07-08	Added: Extra wing to blue building
24-26	06	Changed: Roof – orange to green
24-26	12	Added: Dinghy
24-27	21-28	Changed: Walking couple reversed
24-29	01-04	Added: Flock of birds
27	05-06	Changed: Structure on hilltop enlarged
27	18	Changed: Bag – red to blue
28-29	12-13	Added: Signpost

28-29	28-29	Added: Beachball
28-30	08-09	Added: Water slide
29	14-15	Added: Woman
29-30	07-08	Added: Red building
29-30	11-12	Added: Octopus
29-30	15-16	Changed: Swimming trunks – green to yellow

Puzzle 17: Open Air Pool (page 40)

01-02	20	Added: Slide
01-02	22-23	Changed: Slide to building roof
04	08-09	Removed: Red towel
04-07	03-05	Removed: Path
06	14	Added: Chair
08-09	17	Changed: Umbrella – red to blue
10	07	Removed: White box
11	13	Changed: Rug – black to red
11	19-20	Added: Stingray
11-21	04-12	Added: Plane shadow
12	09-10	Added: Shade tent
13-14	12	Added: Extended path
15	12-13	Added: Walking man
16	24	Added: Swimmer in yellow tube
16-17	01	Added: Extra person
16-17	05-06	Added: Reclining chair
16-17	19-20	Removed: Swimmer with inflatable
17	14	Added: Person in tube
17	27	Removed: Shower pole
17-21	13-15	Added: Extra pool step
17-18	04	Changed: Person rotated
19	04	Removed: Manhole cover
19	29	Changed: Square colour
20-21	30	Removed: Bench
21	23	Changed: Towel size increased
22	17	Changed: Towel – purple to green
22	19	Removed: Woman sunbathing
22-23	02-03	Added: People having a picnic
22-23	06-07	Added: Building extended
23	26	Added: Waste bin
23-24	12-13	Removed: Umbrella shadow
23-26	08-11	Added: Footprint trail
25	10	Removed: Sunbather
25	13	Removed: Boy lying down
25-26	24-25	Removed: Swimmer
25-31	02-07	Added: Path wall
25-35	17	Added: Rope across pool
26-27	27-28	Changed: Sunbathers rotated
26-35	18	Removed: Pool lane marking
27-28	06	Changed: Umbrella – green to purple
27-31	01-02	Changed: Objects and shadows
28-29	08-09	Removed: Glass shelter
29-30	07-08	Added: Reclining chair
31-32	12	Removed: Man by pool edge
32	08-09	Removed: Striped towel
32-33	08-09	Changed: Three towels rotated 90°
34	09-10	Changed: Umbrella colour to all red
34-35	04-06	Added: Tree
34-35	12-13	Added: Pool steps
34-35	19	Changed: Swimming man flipped

Puzzle 18: Graffiti Wall (page 42)

01-02	27-30	Added: Brick wall
01-03	01-03	Added: Ivy
01-04	12-25	Added: Ripped poster
01-10	09-12	Added: Purple graffiti
03-04	28-30	Added: Spray can
05-10	19-22	Added: Black fox
08	09-10	Removed: Canadian flag (maple leaf)
08-09	35	Removed: Leaf
09-10	14-15	Removed: Word "Fine"
09-10	18	Changed: "Alex" to "Axle"
10-13	31-32	Added: Splatter of blue paint
11-12	01-02	Changed: Letter "s" to "p"
11-12	08-09	Changed: Letter "Z" flipped to "N"
11-12	09-11	Removed: Letter "B"
12	17	Changed: Eye – pink to blue
12-14	23-25	Changed: Heart – green to red
13	26	Removed: "E"

20–22	Changed: Heart – pink to yellow
34–35	Added: Leaf
32–33	Added: Cobblestones
01–02	Removed: Green handprint
28–29	Changed: "2010" to "2011"
16–20	Changed: Letter "L" – yellow to blue
27–29	Changed: Heart – pink to green
05	Added: Word "dreamer"
13–17	Removed: Graffito of red spray can
26	Changed: "WIFE" to "KNIFE"
22–28	Added: Streaks of dripping, pink paint
34	Removed: Leaf
05–08	Added: Inverse black "X" and face
04–05	Removed: Green dot
28–29	Added: Arrow
14–15	Removed: Word "LOVE"
27–29	Added: Blue line figure
02–03	Changed: Letter "C" to "O"
06–08	Added: Star
01–06	Added: Blue and green paint splatter
26–35	Added: Road sign
20–21	Removed: Body of bird
11–12	Changed: Face reversed
14–19	Added: Yellow, orange, purple graffito
06	Removed: Pink and yellow graffito
11–12	Removed: Red heart
17–19	Removed: White highlight
01–02	Added: Green handprint
08–11	Added: Green leaf graffito
13–14	Added: Sticker bill
25–26	Changed: Building design – red to white
06–08	Added: Face
21–26	Changed: Segment – green to yellow

Puzzle 19: Park Life (page 44)

24–25	Added: Small tree
34–35	Changed: People rotated
31–32	Added: Stream
28–31	Added: Large tree
21	Added: One person
35	Removed: Waste bins
33–34	Changed: Tree reduced
21	Added: Group of three people
25–26	Changed: Shirt – yellow to pink
33	Changed: Tree – brown to green
15–16	Changed: Increase in size of people
2–13	Removed: Fir tree
01–02	Removed: Fence
26–27	Added: Sink hole
01–03	Changed: Pathways
05–06	Added: Rugby scrum
07	Added: Manhole cover
01	Changed: Shirt – red to green
1–21	Added: Eiffel Tower shadow
13–14	Removed: White blanket
16–17	Changed: Walkers rotated
14	Added: Steps
14–16	Added: Alligator
02	Added: Little fir tree
04	Changed: Blanket – red to blue
20	Removed: Manhole
23–24	Changed: Group size decreased
15–16	Added: People on white picnic blanket
17	Added: Person on bicycle
01	Changed: Flag design
05	Added: Man with red bag
22	Changed: Seated People
27	Added: Group of three people
33	Added: Snake
17–19	Removed: Part of hedge
01–02	Removed: Seat
17–19	Changed: Tree reduce in size
23–24	Removed: Tree
11–14	Added: Tree
01–02	Added: Height to fence
32	Added: Crime scene body outline
13–14	Changed: Tree – blue to green
04–05	Changed: Tree leaves increased
10	Removed: Monument seat

9	Added: Bird
01–03	Removed: Flower border
26–29	Added: Grass to bare ground
15–17	Added: Lamp post
09	Added: Couple sat on bench
15–16	Added: Chimney

Puzzle 20: Pedestrian Crossing (page 46)

11–14	Removed: Bag
20–21	Changed: Shirt stripes blue to red
30	Removed: Manhole cover
20–22	Added: Paper bag
11	Added: Hat
13–14	Changed: Hair – blonde to brown
12–14	Changed: Coat – green to brown
09–10	Removed: Jumper pattern segment
26–27	Changed: Shoes to boots
14	Removed: Tie
08–09	Added: Ponytail
25–30	Added: Excited woman
01–02	Added: Street sign
07	Added: Beard
19–22	Changed: Coat colour red to blue
09	Added: Hat
22–24	Removed: Shopping bag
11–12	Changed: Lady's face
12	Removed: Child's bag
13–14	Removed: Striped top
03–05	Removed: Woman
17	Added: Sun glasses
08	Added: Face mask
14–16	Changed: Bag
03	Changed: Turned head left to right
04	Removed: Colourful T shirt
09–10	Removed: Bag strap
28	Added: Strap on suitcase
07	Added: Woolly hat
02	Changed: Dimmed light
01–07	Changed: Colour of street pole
16–17	Added: Extra hair
03–04	Added: One more traffic light
27	Changed: Dress design – black to red
16–17	Added: Football
11	Changed: Face and hair
06–08	Added: Young man
18–20	Added: Backpack
05	Added: Green hat
01–03	Added: Coloured screen
29–30	Changed: Shoe colour – brown to blue
14–15	Added: Scarf
01–02	Changed: Bag – beige to green
06–08	Added: Turban
	Changed: Man flipped
22–24	Removed: Bag
09–11	Added: Man in hat
01–03	Changed: Colour sign – green to blue
02–04	Added: Statue
14–15	Changed: Bag – orange to green

Puzzle 21: Sports Stadium (page 48)

10	Removed: Stand entrance
26–27	Removed: Dark area of ground
32–33	Changed: Parked car
23–25	Changed: Colour of the crowd
02–04	Removed: Floodlights
23–24	Removed: Black netting
02–03	Removed: Tower
34–35	Added: Lamp post
21–23	Changed: Colour of goalposts
24–25	Added: Camera stage
11	Removed: Round window
01	Removed: Field markings
11	Changed: Fence – red to blue
12–13	Added: Bush
07–08	Changed: Entrance height
17–18	Changed: Writing – red to blue
08–09	Added: New vehicle

31–32	Removed: Wall unit on garage
10–12	Changed: Joined up pathways
25–26	Removed: Canopy
12	Changed: Sign – blue to red
29	Added: Roof unit
10–11	Removed: Roof unit
17	Changed: Colour in grass pattern
07	Changed: Sign – red to green
12–13	Changed: Screen image flipped
13	Removed: Letter
23–24	Removed: Window
31	Removed: Road crossing
30–31	Added: Box crate
34	Changed: Sign – red to yellow
14	Removed: Arched roof
16–17	Changed: Box – red to blue
09–10	Removed: Patch of grass
16	Added: Hat
12	Added: Roof unit
29–31	Added: Tree
09	Removed: Ornamental wall
24–25	Added: Roof extension
14	Removed: Doorway
22	Added: Pillar
08–09	Added: Bush
13	Added: Van
16	Changed: Wall extended
29	Changed: Wall – blue to red
11	Changed: Wall surface
30	Changed: Flowers – red to yellow
28–29	Changed: Fountain
18	Added: Stall canopy
35	Removed: Window

Puzzle 22: Cannes (page 50)

29–30	Changed: Chimney – yellow to blue
14	Removed: Balcony
23–24	Removed: Tile
09–10	Added: Palm tree
15	Removed: Pigeon
12	Changed: Window enlarged
21–23	Removed: Chimney
16	Removed: Air vent
12–13	Changed Window shutter opened
19	Added: Tile layer
15–16	Added: Height to chimney
09	Removed: Building section
07–08	Added: Houses to background
10	Added: Railing
19–20	Removed: Lamp
21–23	Added: Umbrella
10–11	Changed: Building overhang reduced
14–15	Removed: Skylight
18	Removed: Aerial branch
13	Added: Jumping monkey
16–17	Changed: Board – green to purple
16	Removed: Union jack flag
11	Added: Air-conditioning unit
15–16	Added: Curtain
09	Changed: Awning pulled down
17–18	Added: Satellite dish
14	Removed: Air-conditioning unit
15–16	Changed: Flag – blue to yellow
17	Added: Chimney hole
05–07	Changed: Height of tower roof
05–07	Removed: Chimney
07	Changed: Window – purple to green
13–14	Added: Window
14–15	Removed: White wooden frame
18–19	Removed: Chimney
28–30	Added: Man in window
08–09	Added: Tree
12–13	Added: Dormer window
09	Removed: Tree
13	Removed: Chimney skirting
11–12	Removed: Roof decoration
02–03	Added: Hang glider
21–22	Added: Cat
09–10	Added: Extra window

32	15	Added: Pigeon
33-34	11	Changed: Curtain closed
34	03-04	Added: Tower
	06	Added: Cypress tree
	09	Changed: Window
	11	Removed: Window

Puzzle 23: Oranges (page 52)

01	34	Added: Pip
01-06	21-26	Changed: Increased size of orange
02-04	19-20	Added: Leaf
03-06	34-35	Added: Lime
04-16		Added: Leaf
		Added: Stalk
		Removed: Stalk
	26-27	Added: Sticker
03-08	17-21	Changed: White centre reduced
		Changed: Colour of fruit, to red
07-08	15	Added: Stalk
07-08	32	Added: Stalk
	27-32	Added Lemon
	1-12	Changed: Stalk
	07-09	Added: Leaf
09-11	09-11	Added: Cherry
09-11	29-30	Added: Smiley face
	15	Removed: Stalk
	28-31	Changed: Increased leaf size
11-35	18-22	Changed: Peeled orange
12-14	13-18	Changed: Orange's centre enlarged
12-15	04-06	Changed: Leaf – green to orange
13-14	33	Removed: Stalk
14-17	19-23	Added: New fruit
15-16	06-07	Removed: White centre
15-18	31-34	Added: Orange peel
18-19	13-14	Added: Sticker
18-22	01-03	Added: Orange
19-22	25-28	Added: Orange segment
20	0-11	Removed: Pip
23-24	34-35	Added: Orange half
	06-10	Changed: Orange made rotten
21-22	30-31	Added: Leaf
22	12-13	Removed: Stalk
22-23	22-23	Changed: Size of stalk
22	03-04	Added: Pip
23-25	25-27	Removed: Orange
23-27	09-13	Changed: Orange flipped
23-27	19-23	Added: Lemon
24-25	05-07	Changed: Background, to green
24-27	15-17	Added: Leaf
	14-15	Added: Stalk
25-26	24	Added: Stamp
25-28	02-05	Added: Lime half
25-29	27-30	Changed: Fruit colour to yellow
25-25	33-35	Changed: Colour increased
27-28	18-19	Added: Orange segment
27-30	12-15	Added: Lemon half
29-30	05	Removed: Stalk
29-30	32	Changed: Leaf colour

Puzzle 24: Shopping Mall (page 54)

02	06-13	Changed: Window frame colour
03	27-28	Changed: Fire extinguisher – red to yellow
03-04	06	Changed: Sign – green to red
04	02	Removed: Shirt pattern
04-05	03-06	Changed: Woman to man
04-06	14-18	Changed: Couple flipped
05	31-32	Removed: Poster on wall
07		Changed: Direction of arrow
07	05-06	Added: Suitcase
07	34-35	Added: Hair with ponytail
08-09	13	Changed: Shoe to sandal
10	06-07	Added: Backpack
10	26-27	Changed: Shirt – purple to yellow
10	30-31	Added: Boot
10	13-14	Removed: Light cover
10-11	15-18	Removed: Woman
10-12	04-05	Changed: Floor covering

10-11	11	Added: Extra rail
	02	Removed: Shop name
	18-21	Changed: Woman flipped
12-13	02-04	Removed: Light panel
13	17-18	Changed: Direction of arrow
13	20-21	Added: Red tie
14-15	33-34	Changed: Sign – green to red
13	06	Changed: Shirt – pink to green
13	15-19	Removed: Sign on post
13-15	05-06	Added: Red chequered shirt
13	03-06	Added: Person on escalator
13	20	Removed: Word on shirt
17-18	13-14	Added: Backpack
13-18	31-32	Changed: Shirt stripe colour
18-19	09-11	Added: Plant
18-19	12	Removed: Writing on shirt
18-19	05-07	Changed: Shop sign – green to red
20	18	Added: Hat
20-21	23-24	Changed: Shirt pattern, to white
21	09-10	Changed: Shirt – pink to orange
21	24-25	Removed: Identity badge
21	26	Added: Paper bag
	06-07	Added: Lighting fixture
	14-17	Removed: Woman on escalator
	21-22	Added: Image to screen
23-27	22-23	Removed: White flooring
25-28	14	Changed: Logo – pink to blue
25-25	30-33	Added: Woman
26	25	Changed: Bag – yellow to black
27-28	01-02	Changed: Direction of logo
27-28	03-05	Added: Wall
28-29	16-23	Changed: Light panel – to pink
30	20-21	Removed: Logo

Puzzle 25: Delicatessen (page 56)

01-02	05-08	Added: Salami
02-04	09-10	Changed: Jar lid cover – blue to red
04-05	09-12	Removed: Striped string
05	22-23	Changed: Lid cover – red to green
06-08	08-10	Changed: Label
06-08	20-21	Changed: Lid colour black to red
09	19	Changed: Bottle lid – red to black
09	25	Removed: Orange label image
09-10	23-24	Changed: Label
	30	Changed: Fruit – yellow to red
10-11	07-08	Removed: Label
10-11	14-15	Changed: Label – red to blue
10-12	28-29	Removed: Fruit
12	26-27	Added: Cat
12	30	Removed: Packet
12-14	04-08	Added: Hanging meat
13-14	24-25	Changed: Packet
13-14	26-27	Changed: Poster image
14	18-19	Removed: Sausage
14	24-25	Added: Packet of cheese
14-15	21-22	Removed: Tin
15	20-21	Removed: Shelf support
15	21-22	Added: Bottle
15	21	Added: Cheese
16-17	23-24	Changed: Label – red to yellow
16-17	24	Removed: Cheese
17	06	Removed: Label
17-18	22-23	Added: Hanging package
18-19	18-20	Added: Sausage
19-20	17-19	Removed: Light
20-21	24-25	Added: Meat patties
20-22	26	Added: Mouse
21-22	11-12	Removed: Security camera
21-22	13-15	Added: Hanging bottle
22	07-08	Added: Label
22	22	Added: Small fruit
23	22-23	Changed: Bottle label
23-24	26-27	Added: Hanging package
24	17-18	Changed: Label – yellow to purple
24	24	Changed: Circle on label – blue to red
24-27	29-30	Changed: Cardboard sheet reduced
26-27	06-09	Removed: Hanging meat
26-27		Removed: Green striped string
28-29	11-13	Removed: Wrapped meat

29-30	21-22	Added: Jar
30-31		Added: Label
33-34	24-26	Changed: Label – yellow to green
33-35	06-08	Changed: Chili pepper – red to green
33-35	14-15	Changed: Letter
34	20-21	Removed: Label

Puzzle 26: Supermarket (page 58)

01-02	01	Removed: Hanging light
01-02	05-06	Added: Window in door
01-02	29-30	Removed: Logo
02-03	04	Removed: Sign letter
02-03	05	Changed: Sign lettering – red to blue
03	13-14	Changed: Sign – red to blue
04	01-02	Removed: Hanging fixture
04	24	Removed: Sign lettering
04-05	09-10	Changed: Trolley to child's pram
04-06	02-03	Changed: Bird outline green to blue
06-06	12-15	Changed: Man flipped
05-06	19-20	Added: Bag
	16	Added: Hat
06-07	10-13	Removed: Man with trolley
06-08	14-15	Changed: Bag to guitar
08	10-11	Changed: Pram – blue to yellow
10	19-20	Removed: Strap
10-11	02-04	Added: Banner
11	05-06	Changed: Machine – green to red
11-12	15-16	Added: Hat
11-12	28	Added: Glasses
12	05-06	Removed: Hanging camera
12	12-13	Added: Bin
13	20-22	Changed: Trousers – red to blue
12-14	14-16	Changed: Trousers to shorts
13	03-04	Changed: Sign – yellow to red
13-15	10-11	Changed: Apron – red to blue
15	04	Changed: Toilet sign
18	08	Changed: Stripes – black to red
18	08	Removed: Checkout screen
16-17	16-18	Changed: Woman's hair
	10	Added: Stacked lights
17-18	07-08	Removed: Shelf
18	05	Changed: Arrow rotated
18	15-16	Changed: Hair – red to grey
18-19	22-24	Changed: Bin size decreased
19-20	06-08	Changed: Items on shelf
19-20	02-03	Removed: Window
21	08-09	Changed: Shirt – blue to pink
22-23	01-02	Removed: Hanging fixture
22-23	18-20	Changed: Screen made opaque
24	15-18	Changed: Height of bar
25	11-12	Changed: Screen colour – red to blue
25-26	25-27	Changed: Bag
25-26	07-10	Removed: Clothes
26-29	28-29	Changed: Floor tile – green to red
26-29	19-21	Changed: Coat – red to blue
23-28	04	Added: boxes
23-28	09	Added: boxes
28-30	11-13	Added: Man

Puzzle 27: Sports Fans (page 60)

02-03	33-35	Added: Hand with horn
03	20-22	Removed: Half of scarf
03-05	05-08	Changed: Flag stripe – blue to green
03-05	23-25	Added: Foam hand
04-05	02-03	Changed: Face
05-06	12	Changed: Camera to hat
05-06	22	Removed: Flag
05-06	34-35	Changed: Face
06-07	09	Changed: Hat – yellow to white
06-07	13-14	Added: Beer bottle
06-08	26-29	Removed: Bag
07-08	04-06	Removed: Camera
07-10	17-21	Added: Smoke
08	11	Removed: Little footballs
08-10	13-14	Added hat
08-11	09-12	Changed: Shirt – red to blue
09-10	16	Removed: Logo

09-10	21-24	Changed: Horn – green to orange
09-11	27-28	Added: Shirt number
12-13	01	Removed: Face
12-13	17	Added: Sunglasses
12-14	18-19	Added: Orange wig
12-14	27-30	Removed: Words
13	09-10	Changed: Colour of hat
13-14	15-18	Changed: Stripes – red to blue
14-15	05-06	Removed: Beer bottle
14-15	25-26	Added: Hat
15-16	01-02	Added: Shirt lettering
15-16	10-13	Removed: Woman
15-16	33-34	Changed: Face
16	30	Changed: Flag segment – black to red
17-18	02-03	Changed: Balloon – orange to blue
18-19	21-23	Changed: Horn – blue to red
19-31	34	Removed: Horn
19-20	19-20	Added: Hat
19-20	21-23	Changed: Stripe – black to white
20	11-13	Removed: Arm
20-21	04	Added: Hat
22	15-16	Changed: Face
22-24	12-14	Added: Bubble
23-24	05-06	Removed: Shirt sleeve
23-25	01-04	Added: Arm
24-25	03-05	Removed: Shirt writing
24-26	30-32	Changed: Camera to horn
25	14-15	Added: White cap
25	02-03	Added: Sunglasses
	24-25	Added: Flag
26-28	28-30	Added: Boy
26-29	17-23	Added: Man
28-29	30	Changed: Armband – green to yellow

Puzzle 28: Construction Site (page 62)

01-02	19-21	Remove: Puddle
02-03	13	Removed: Scaffolding support
02-03	19-21	Added: Wood in mud
04-05	23-24	Removed: Metal object
04-05	20	Removed: Ladder bars
05	16-17	Removed: Iron bar
05	09	Changed: Top of barrel
05	24-25	Removed: Yellow bar
06-07	19-23	Added: Metal beam height
07-09	10-11	Added: Man
08-09	24	Removed: Rope
08-09	24-26	Removed: Puddle
09-10	07-08	Added: Scaffolding frame
09	14-17	Removed: Iron bar support
09-10	21	Changed: Jeans – blue to orange
10	22-24	Added: Extended iron bar
10-11	22-23	Removed: Piece of wood
10-12	01-03	Added: Height to column
11	18-19	Added: Iron bar
11-12	05	Added: Grafitti fox added
12	21-23	Changed: Machine yellow to green
12-14	07-09	Changed: Scaffolding – yellow to red
13-14	29	Added: Piece of wood
13-15	11-12	Added: Alligator
14-15	24	Changed: Object – red to green
14-15	28-29	Added: Extended sheet
14-16	20-23	Removed: Yellow bar
15-17	06-07	Removed: Scaffolding frame
16-18	25-27	Changed: Bar – black to white
17-18	21-22	Changed: Hose – yellow to blue
18	26-27	Removed: Part of wooden plank
18	25-26	Removed: Box
20	19	Added: Boot
21-22	22-23	Added: Wood pile
23	25-27	Removed: Vertical wooden beam
24	07-09	Changed: Edge – yellow to blue
24-25	02-03	Added: Warning sign
24-25	12-13	Removed: Wooden board
24-26	26-28	Added: Iron bar
25-26	07-08	Removed: White bag
26	24	Removed: Rope
28	23-24	Added: White bag
28-29	29-30	Added: Yellow bar
29-30	14	Added: Wooden sheet
30	24-27	Added: Vertical plank
29-30	07-08	Added: Piece of wood
30-31	27-30	Added: Yellow frames
30-32	12-13	Changed: Wooden sheet – brown to green
32-33	21-23	Removed: Iron bar
33-34	02-04	Removed: Iron bar on wall

Puzzle 29: Venice (page 64)

01-06	28-29	Added: Crack in paving stones
02-03	11-12	Changed: Paving stone darkened
02-03	21	Added: Weeds
03-04	09-10	Added: Pigeon
03-04	22-24	Added: Disabled Parking sign
05	14	Removed: Pigeon
05	17	Removed: Crack in paving
05	29	Removed: Paper
05-07	34-35	Added: Two people
06	13	Removed: Pigeon
07-08	21-22	Changed: Shirt – red to blue
09-10	09-12	Removed: Woman in green hat
09-10	10-12	Changed: T-shirt – orange to violet
10	22	Changed: Hair – ginger to blonde
10	34-35	Added: Plastic bag
11-12	15	Removed: Pigeon
11-12	20-25	Removed: Child
11-12	31-32	Added: Hole in ground (note hand)
11-13	01-05	Changed: Crack in paving extended
11-14	15-16	Removed: Painted paving stones
12-13	14	Removed: Pigeon's shadow
13-15	01-05	Changed: Colour of shadow – to green
13-15	06-07	Changed: Direction of paving stones
13-15	30-31	Added: Manhole cover
13-17	17-18	Changed: Trousers – orange to blue
14	12-13	Removed: Pigeon
15-16	02-04	Changed: Paving stones lightened
15	19	Added: Pigeon
15	23	Removed: Bag
16	09	Changed: Shirt – blue to yellow
16	31	Added: Handbag
16-17	06-07	Changed: Bird
18-23	20-27	Added: Hopscotch
19	01-02	Added: Hat
19	09	Changed: Piece of paper enlarged
19	10	Added: Pigeon on hand
19	17	Removed: Piece of paper
19-20	03-04	Added: Boots
22	05	Added: Blue hat
22-23	06-07	Changed: Camera enlarged
24-25	20-21	Changed: Man now floating off ground
25-26	01	Changed: Paving stones
25-26	34-35	Changed: Backpack – orange to purple
26	11-13	Changed: Girl reversed, to face left
26	21-22	Changed: Paving surface broken
26-27	04-05	Added: Cat
27-28	33-35	Added: Box
28	13	Removed: Pigeon
28	32	Added: Dollar bill
29-30	01-07	Changed: Woman and shadow reversed

Puzzle 30: Stars and Space (page 66)

01-02	12	Added: UFO
01	32	Removed: Star
03	16	Added: Star
03	26	Added: Star
03-04	18	Removed: Star
04-05	09	Removed: Star
05	26	Removed: Star
05-06	01	Added: Star
06	14	Added: Star
08-09	10-11	Added: Helix nebula
09	33	Removed: Star
09-10	31	Added: Planet
10	34	Added: Star
10-11	17	Added: Star
10-13	01-04	Added: Constellation of Taurus
11-12	25-26	Removed: Star
12-14	10	Added: Shooting star
13	21	Removed: Star
13	29	Added: Astronaut
14	10-11	Removed: Star
14	11	Removed: Star
14-15	24-25	Added: Star
16	03	Added: Star
16-17	31-32	Added: Star
17	35	Removed: Star
17-18	25	Added: Star
18	05	Removed: Star
18	12	Added: Star
19	08	Added: Star
20	26	Removed: Star
20-21	02	Added: Star
20-21	30-31	Removed: Star
21	18-19	Added: Star
20-22	08-09	Removed: Gaseous nebula
23	02	Removed: Star
23-24	14-15	Added: Meteor
24	03	Removed: Star
24	07	Added: Star
24-25	13	Added: Star
24-25	17-18	Removed: Star
24-25	30-31	Removed: Star
25	26	Removed: Star
25	27	Added: Star
25-27	22-23	Added: Star
26	02	Added: Saturn
26-27	33-34	Added: Galaxy
27	34-35	Added: Star
27-29	10-11	Added: Galaxy
28	03-04	Removed: Star
28	19-20	Added: Star

Puzzle 31: Coney Island (page 68)

01-02	13	Added: Hinge
02	03	Removed: Red shadow around "M"
02-03	01	Changed: Ice cream, to yellow
02-03	14-15	Changed: Colour of popcorn
03-04	08	Added: Cherry
03-04	13	Removed: Rivet
03	20-22	Removed: Lollipop stick
03-05	25-26	Removed: Stripe of yellow paint
04	06	Removed: Word "AND"
04	10-11	Removed: Number "50" (underlined)
05-06	03-04	Changed: "SALES TAX" sign enlarged
05-11	08-11	Added: Height to box of waffle cones
06	22	Changed: Number "4" to "3"
08-09	29-30	Changed: Inner circle – red to yellow
09	15-16	Changed: "$" to "£"
09-10	13	Removed: Waffle cone
09-11	32-33	Removed: Yellow highlight
10	17	Removed: Black foot of cabinet
10-11	03	Changed: "N" moved, to read "AN ICE"
11-13	12	Removed: Blue writing on top of cone
11-14	07-11	Changed: Ice cream swirl reversed
12	01-02	Changed: Letter "Y" to "I"
13-14	26-27	Added: Red star
14	16	Added: Rest of letter "F"
14-22	02-06	Changed: Neon sign – blue to orange
15	15-16	Changed: Colour on tin – blue to red
15	21-22	Removed: Yellow line
15-17	23-24	Removed: Reflected letters "Lem"
16	14-16	Removed: Lollipop stick
16	17-18	Added: Stripe of blue/yellow paint
17	06	Changed: Eye reversed
18	27-31	Added: Yellow stripe to letter "L"
18-19	11	Changed: Candyfloss – blue to pink
18-21	16	Changed: Colour of stand – blue to green
19	12-13	Removed: Candy-stick
20	01	Removed: Chain
20	11-12	Added: Length to candy-stick
20-21	29-30	Changed: Letter "o" filled in black
20-22	22	Removed: Red swish
21-22	17-19	Changed: Drink bottle
22	19-20	Removed: Letter "e"
22-23	11-13	Removed: Electric cable
23-24	03-04	Removed: Can
24-25	33-34	Changed: Red swirl reversed

95

Column 1

21-22	Changed: Bus stripe – yellow to green
26	Added: Bag carrier to bus roof
32-34	Added: Man in side car
19-20	Removed car
	Changed: Number plate – yellow to black
2-13	Removed: Tower
08-13	Changed: Building stripe – orange to grey
16	Changed: Words flipped
22-23	Removed: Green traffic light
13-14	Added: Sunlight strip to roof
28-30	Added: Lamp post arm
21-24	Removed: Traffic light
27	Removed: Advert on bus
16	Changed: Sign – green to red
17-18	Changed: Car – red to blue
12-13	Removed: Building
14-15	Removed: Turret
22-23	Added: Car
15	Changed: Sign
31	Removed: Blue bag
21-22	Added: Man on bike
26	Changed: Shirt – Blue to yellow
23	Changed: Crossing enhanced
14-15	Changed: Window decoration
25	Added: Roof rack
27-28	Removed: Letter
32-35	Removed: Poles
11-12	Removed: Window
34-35	Changed: Clothing – purple to green
26-27	Removed: Bicycle
29-31	Added: Man with backpack
09-10	Added: Turret
22	Changed: Bus markings – yellow to green

Puzzle 37:
Sailing Regatta (page 80)

13-14	Added: Boat
08-09	Added: Sail
15-16	Added: Boat
09	Removed: Boat
11-13	Added: Sail
08	Changed: Sail extended
23-27	Changed: Sail – yellow to red
14-15	Changed: Boat
23	Removed: Letter
32-34	Added: Whale
12-14	Added: Rock extended
07	Added: Sail
05	Changed: Lighthouse height
14-15	Changed: Sail
21-22	Removed: Sail
11-12	Added: Easter Island statue
20	Added: Boat
06-07	Added: Loch Ness monster
07	Removed: Yacht
14	Added: Sinking boat
20-21	Added: Pirate flag
19	Removed: White wake
08	Changed: Boat direction
05-06	Added: Ocean liner
7	Added: "7"
18-19	Added: Dinghy
26	Added: Dinghy
21-23	Removed: Sail
14	Removed: Boat
14-16	Added: Octopus
21-27	Changed: Yacht direction
7	Removed: Small boat
10-11	Removed: Red object
06-07	Added: Boat
33-34	Added: Man
24-25	Changed: Boat hull – orange to blue
06-07	Changed: Boat direction
17-18	Added: Sail
16	Changed: Boat direction
18-20	Added: Windsurfer
18-22	Changed: Boat size increased
26-30	Removed: Rigging flags
11	Added: Rock sculpture
25	Added: Orange flag

Column 2

14	Added: Boat
09	Added: Yacht
13	Removed: Small boat
16-17	Changed: Boat – red to yellow
11	Added: Shipwreck
14-19	Changed: Boat reduced
08-10	Added: Power pole
06-07	Added: Sail
15	Changed: Boat – green to white
06	Changed: Rock height
17-18	Removed: Boat
17	Removed: Boat
19-20	Changed: Boat direction
06	Added: Yacht
26	Added: Dolphin
05-06	Added: Building
05	Added: Cliff extended
07	Removed: Yacht
10	Changed: Sail – orange to white
13-14	Added: Buoy marker
15-16	Removed: Boat
06	Changed: Yacht to rock
13	Changed: Boat direction
07	Removed: Yacht
11-12	Removed: Boat
07-08	Removed: Yacht
08	Added: Small yacht
12-13	Removed: Yacht
18	Added: Boat
10-11	Changed: Sail – red to green
07-08	Added: Rock extended
16	Changed: Boat – white to orange
18-19	Changed: Sail – brown to white
18	Changed: Boat – orange to white
23-24	Added: Water skier
10-11	Added: Rock Climber
16-17	Removed: Boat
14-16	Added: Sail
16-17	Removed: Small boat
01-07	Added: Castle
20-21	Added: Boat
16-19	Changed: Boat direction
09-14	Added: Waterfall
08	Added: Cave
16	Added: Boat
06	Removed: Rock headland
17-18	Added: Container
32-34	Added: Bird
01-04	Added: Waterspout
12-13	Added: Bird
08-09	Added: Rock
20	Removed: Boat
16-17	Removed: Boat
05	Added: Chimney
15-16	Changed: Boat direction
16-18	Added: Boat

Puzzle 38:
Tourist Beach (page 84)

31-32	Removed: Fence post
18-19	Added: Man in chair
20-22	Changed: Group flipped
11	Removed: Yellow towel
14	Changed: Towel – blue to green
33	Changed: Umbrella segment – green to purple
15	Removed: Towel
23-24	Changed: Man flipped
28-29	Removed: Man
18-19	Added: Beach tent
30	Removed: Shadow
20-21	Removed: Sign
15-16	Added: Couple
22-23	Removed: Umbrella
33	Removed: Boy
21-22	Added: Man
13-15	Removed: Tent awning
34-35	Added: Child
20	Added: Towel
07	Changed: Sunbather

Column 3

12-13	Changed: Tent – blue to green
11	Removed: Towel
23	Removed: Umbrella
26-27	Added: Man on towel
27-28	Removed: Woman
03-04	Changed: Woman flipped
02	Changed: Tent – blue to white
27-28	Changed: Umbrella – red to blue
16-18	Changed: Pole extended
22	Added: Umbrella
19	Changed: Inner tube segment – red to blue
33-34	Changed: People flipped
30-31	Removed: Towel
11	Changed: Towel – blue to red
19	Added: Woman on towel
15-16	Added: Woman
28-29	Removed: Chair
12	Changed: Woman flipped
28-29	Changed: Windbreak – red to yellow
05-06	Changed: Tent – blue to pink
15	Added: Man on towel
24-25	Changed: Woman moved
19-20	Added: Umbrella
26-27	Changed: Person sitting flipped
07	Changed: Group flipped
10-11	Added: Business suit
02	Added: People on towel
15	Added: Woman on towel
03-04	Removed: Figure
04	Added: Beach chair
18	Added: Lifeguard tube
05	Removed: Woman
31-32	Added: Person sitting
34-45	Added: Sandcastle
13-14	Changed: Towel – blue to yellow
22-23	Removed: man
14-17	Changed: Flag flipped
03	Changed: Surfboard – yellow to red
06-07	Added: Man running
24-25	Changed: Umbrella
16-17	Added: Umbrella and shadow
10	Changed: Shorts – red to blue
33-34	Added: Woman with bucket
01	Changed: Woman flipped
19-20	Changed: Umbrella segment – purple to orange
07	Removed: Towel
14	Changed: Man flipped
10	Changed: Towel pile to chill box
01-02	Removed: People on towel
08-09	Added: Woman
25-26	Added: Woman
32-33	Changed: Umbrella – orange to blue
15	Removed: Kneeling child
06-07	Changed: Woman flipped
24	Removed: Towel
04-05	Added: Man
27	Removed: Man on towel
01	Changed: Man on towel moved
11-12	Changed: Towel – blue to red
13	Added: Child
23-34	Changed: Umbrella – green to purple
19	Removed: Shadow
11-12	Added: Sign
08-09	Changed: Woman flipped
25	Removed: Shadow
07-09	Removed: Man
20-21	Changed: Couple flipped
30-31	Changed: Man flipped
13	Added: Walrus
17-18	Changed: Woman flipped
20-21	Removed: Man
04-05	Added: Man with board
03-04	Added: Man
07-08	Added: Man
17-25	Added: Kite surfer
23-24	Removed: Child
28-29	Changed: Man submerged
29-31	Removed: Man
08-10	Added: Whale
12-13	Added: Boat